LIVE. LEARN. DISCOVER.

Bath · New York · Singapore · Hong Kong · Cologne · Delhi · Melbourne

Jaguar Word Search

Help this jaguar find some food with the word puzzle below! The hidden words are all animals that jaguars like to hunt down and eat.

- CROCODILES
- DEER
- FOXES
- MONKEYS
- SHEEP
- CATTLE
- TURTLES
- TAPIRS
- BIRDS
- FISH

D	E	E	R	D	T	R	Y	I	O	P
A	D	G	J	K	A	L	Z	X	E	C
N	M	Q	E	T	P	U	I	E	P	F
T	A	P	I	R	S	Q	H	S	F	O
H	K	M	L	Z	C	S	B	O	M	X
C	R	O	C	O	D	I	L	E	S	E
A	P	N	I	Y	R	E	J	L	R	S
T	A	K	F	L	Q	J	Z	Q	E	R
T	C	E	I	T	U	R	T	L	E	S
L	C	Y	S	A	L	E	L	S	P	R
E	G	S	H	B	I	R	D	S	A	Q

DiscoveryFact™
Jaguars kill their prey by piercing its skull with their long, sharp canine teeth. They are one of the strongest "big cats" in the world.

Tiger Trouble

These tigers are stalking a deer for dinner. Help them chase it through the maze as quickly as possible!

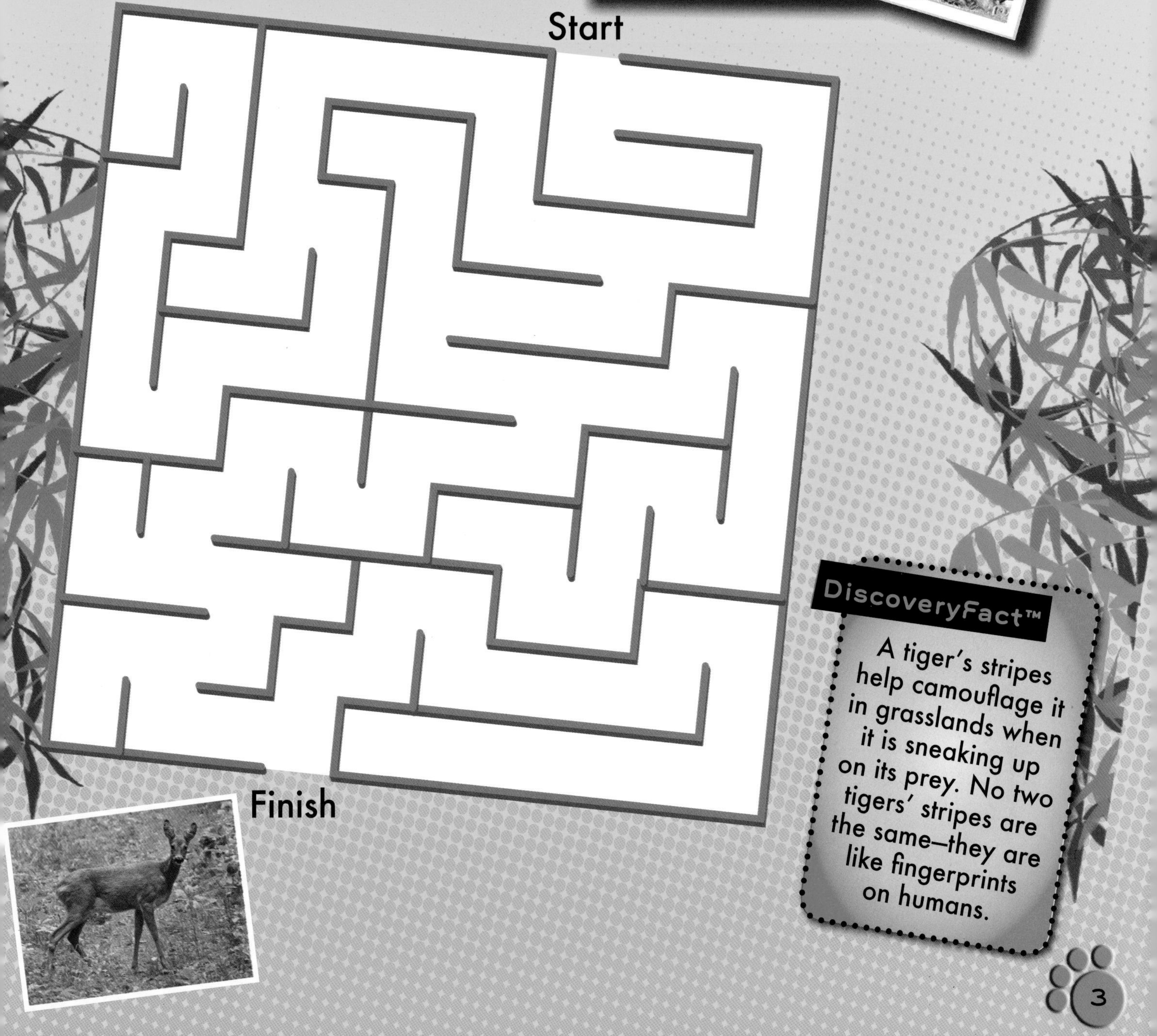

DiscoveryFact™

A tiger's stripes help camouflage it in grasslands when it is sneaking up on its prey. No two tigers' stripes are the same—they are like fingerprints on humans.

Cheetah Code

Use the code breaker to translate the coded message below and discover a cool fact about cheetahs!

A	B	C	D	E	F	G	H	I	J	K	L	M
N	O	P	Q	R	S	T	U	V	W	X	Y	Z

DiscoveryFact™

A cheetah can accelerate to 40 miles per hour in just three strides.

Lion Tangle

This lion is looking for somewhere to have a drink on the savanna. Can you tell which pathway leads to the watering hole?

A B C

DiscoveryFact™

Lions have very powerful front legs, and can break a zebra's back wth a single blow from their huge paws.

The correct path is ___.

Lynx Odd-One-Out

Take a close look at the group of lynxes below. One of them isn't the same as the others. Can you circle the odd one out?

A

B

C

D

E

F

G

DiscoveryFact™

The lynx uses its powerful sense of smell to hunt its prey. It has such a sensitive nose that it can smell an animal it wants to eat from about 1,000 feet away.

Leopard Scramble

An exciting fact about leopards has been scrambled up below. Can you re-arrange the letters to reveal it?

s e o a r p d L   i h e d   r h i e t

L _ _ _ _ _ _ _ _   h _ _ _   t _ _ _ _ _

y p e r   n i   s t e r e

p _ _ _   i _   t _ _ _ _ _

DiscoveryFact™

Leopards don't like other leopards coming onto their patch of land. They leave scratch marks on trees to scare each other off—and will fight if they meet by accident!

Now find a sticker that matches the fact you revealed and put it here.

Bengal Tiger Puzzle

Find the correct stickers to complete this Bengal tiger puzzle. Use the picture clues below to help.

DiscoveryFact™

Bengal tigers can be white or orange. The white tigers are rarer, and are often even larger than normal orange tigers.

Cougar Shadows

These cougars and their shadows have gotten mixed up. Draw lines to match each cougar to the correct shadow.

A

B

C

1

2

3

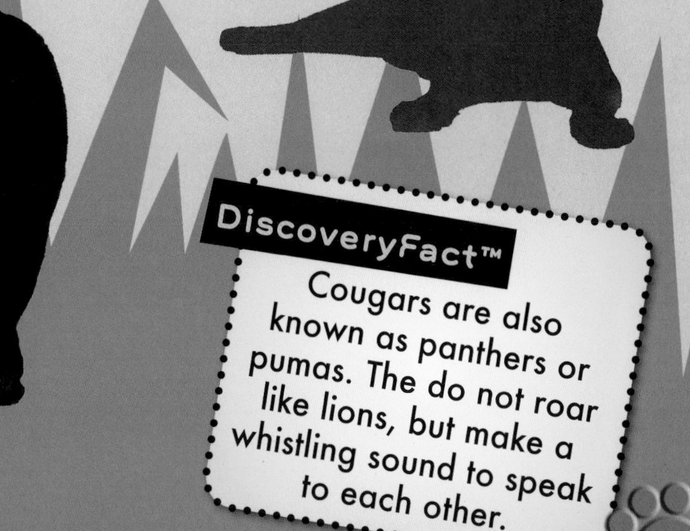

DiscoveryFact™

Cougars are also known as panthers or pumas. The do not roar like lions, but make a whistling sound to speak to each other.

Big Cat Fact Files

Find the correct stickers to complete these fact files!

Jaguar

Scientific Name: *Panthera onca*

Found: Rainforests

Prey: Deer, tapirs, foxes, dogs, snakes

Special Weapon: Enormous strength, speed

Tiger

Scientific Name: *Panthera tigris*

Found: Open grasslands and swamps

Prey: Deer, buffalo, boar

Special Weapon: Powerful paw swipe

Cheetah

Scientific Name: *Acinonyx jubatus*

Found: African savanna

Prey: Gazelles, zebras

Special Weapon: Incredible speed

Lion

Scientific Name: *Panthera leo*

Found: Savannas and grasslands

Prey: Wildebeest, boar, zebras, impalas

Special Weapons: Huge strength and enormous jaws

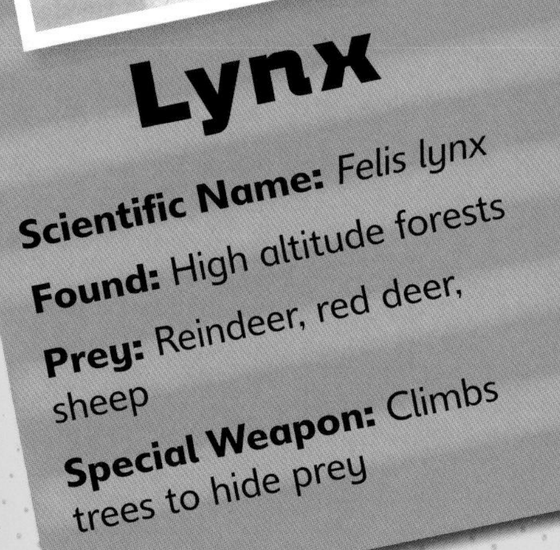

Lynx

Scientific Name: *Felis lynx*

Found: High altitude forests

Prey: Reindeer, red deer, sheep

Special Weapon: Climbs trees to hide prey

Leopard

Scientific Name: *Panthera pardus*

Found: From rainforests to deserts

Prey: Monkeys, antelopes, gazelles

Special Weapon: Silently stalks then pounces on prey

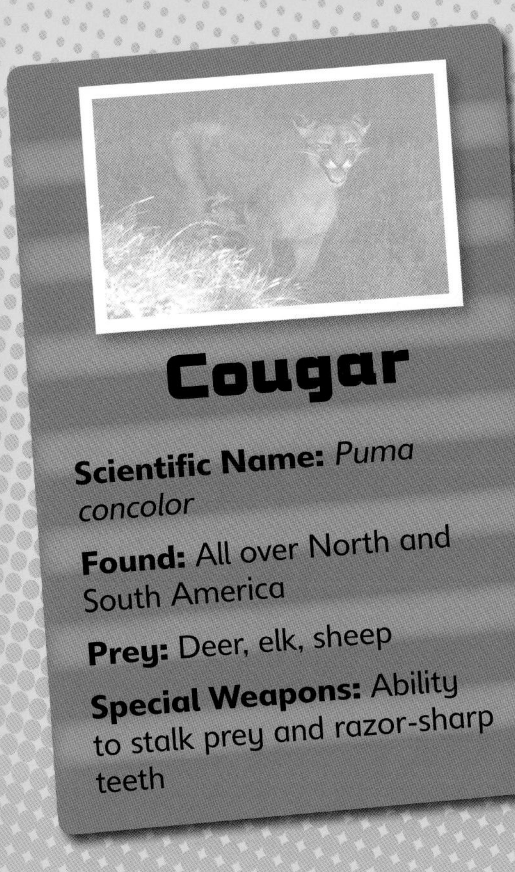

Cougar

Scientific Name: *Puma concolor*

Found: All over North and South America

Prey: Deer, elk, sheep

Special Weapons: Ability to stalk prey and razor-sharp teeth

Bengal Tiger

Scientific Name: *Panthera tigris tigris*

Found: Asian rainforests and grasslands

Prey: Boar, buffalo, rhino

Special Weapon: Killer bite to the throat

Brown Bear Hidden Message

Cross out the numbers in the table below, then copy the remaining letters into the boxes to discover some cool facts about brown bears.

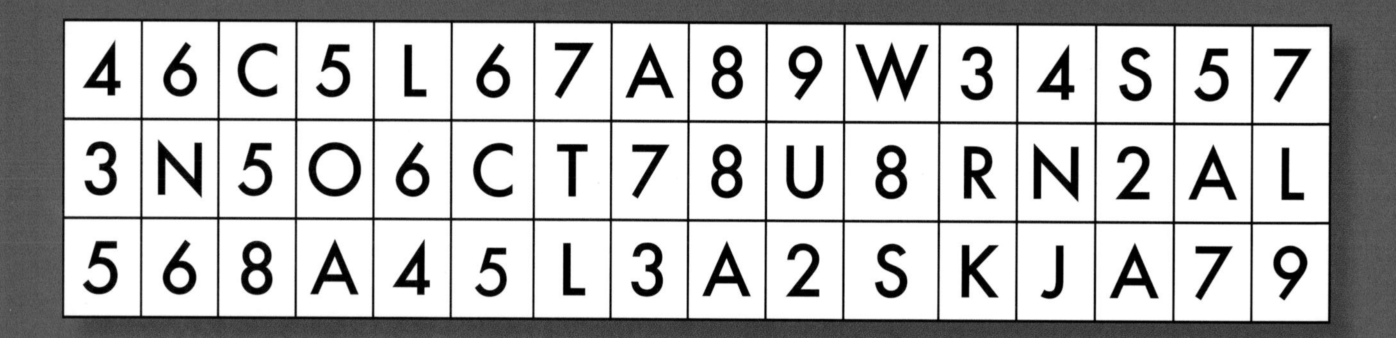

4	6	C	5	L	6	7	A	8	9	W	3	4	S	5	7
3	N	5	O	6	C	T	7	8	U	8	R	N	2	A	L
5	6	8	A	4	5	L	3	A	2	S	K	J	A	7	9

A brown bear's most deadly weapon is its _ _ _ _ _.

Brown bears are _ _ _ _ _ _ _ _ _ _ _ _ _.

95 percent of the U.S. brown bear population lives in _ _ _ _ _ _ _ _.

DiscoveryFact™

Along with polar bears, brown bears are the largest carnivores (meat eaters) on land. Despite their size, they normally only eat small prey like fish and small animals.

Polar Bear Word Search

Can you find the 10 words below in the squares? They are all things that a polar bear would see in its polar habitat.

Q	A	T	G	Y	F	U	I	I	O	P
L	R	H	L	F	I	S	A	C	Z	X
I	C	B	A	N	S	M	G	E	S	E
C	T	U	C	O	H	K	O	U	U	G
E	I	K	I	S	N	O	W	V	D	A
B	C	L	E	Y	T	S	C	A	V	E
E	F	T	R	U	I	O	P	L	J	G
R	O	R	E	I	N	D	E	E	R	A
G	X	B	C	Z	X	V	N	J	G	D
S	A	E	T	G	S	E	A	L	U	T
Y	E	S	E	A	N	Y	F	S	D	C

ICE
SNOW
ICEBERG
SEA
FISH
GLACIER
SEAL
REINDEER
CAVE
ARCTIC FOX

DiscoveryFact™

Polar bears often hunt by standing over breathing holes in the ice. When a seal pops up for air, the bear breaks through the ice and kills the seal with its powerful jaws.

Buffalo Find-the-Difference

Can you find the four differences between the two water buffalo pictures below?

What is a running herd of buffalo called?

Write the answer here: S________

(Take a look at the fact to the right for a clue!)

DiscoveryFact™

Buffalo fight off predators by gathering the whole herd together to attack. They can use their horns to fight with, and can trample smaller animals underfoot when they are stampeding.

Rhinoceros Puzzle

Finish off the picture of a rhinoceros below by adding the tail, horn, and ears stickers in the right places! Use the picture clues below to help.

DiscoveryFact™

A rhinoceros's horn is made of densely packed hair, not bone—but it is still very dangerous!

Bull Tangle

This bull is charging across a field at full speed. But which line leads to the gate? Follow each one to find out.

A B C

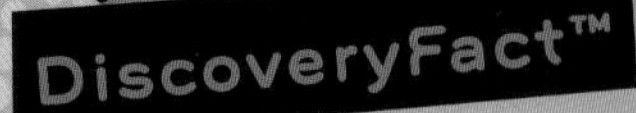

DiscoveryFact™

Bulls are one of the most dangerous domestic (non-wild) animals in the world. They charge when they think they are in danger and can kill people with their sharp horns.

The correct line is ___ .

Gorilla Hidden Message

Cross out the numbers in the table below, then copy the remaining letters into the boxes to discover the special name given to male gorillas because of the fur on their backs.

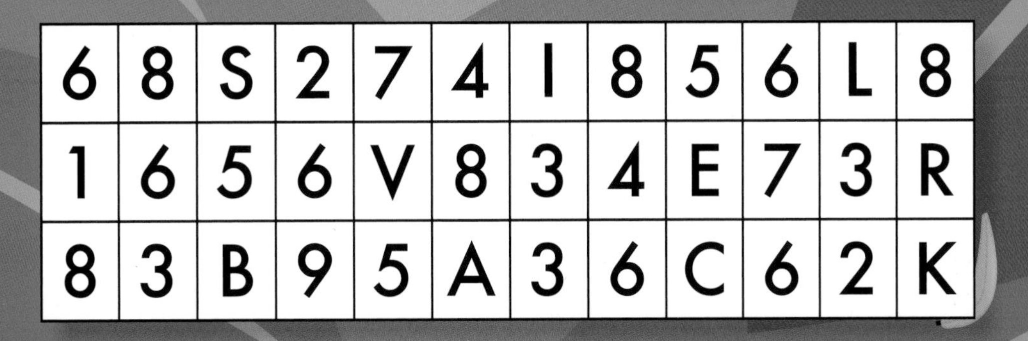

6	8	S	2	7	4	I	8	5	6	L	8
1	6	5	6	V	8	3	4	E	7	3	R
8	3	B	9	5	A	3	6	C	6	2	K

DiscoveryFact™

Gorillas are very similar to humans. They have fingerprints like us, and are very intelligent.

There are ten bananas hidden on this page! See if you can find them!

Elk Antler Match

Elks each have unique antlers. Match the pairs of antlers below—but watch out. One antler doesn't have a partner!

A

B

C

D

E

F

G

DiscoveryFact™

Elks can be very dangerous when they are protecting their young. They can use their big antlers as weapons to attack humans or other animals they see as a threat.

Hippopotamus Odd-One-Out

Take a close look at the group of hippos below. One of them isn't the same as the others. Can you circle the odd one out?

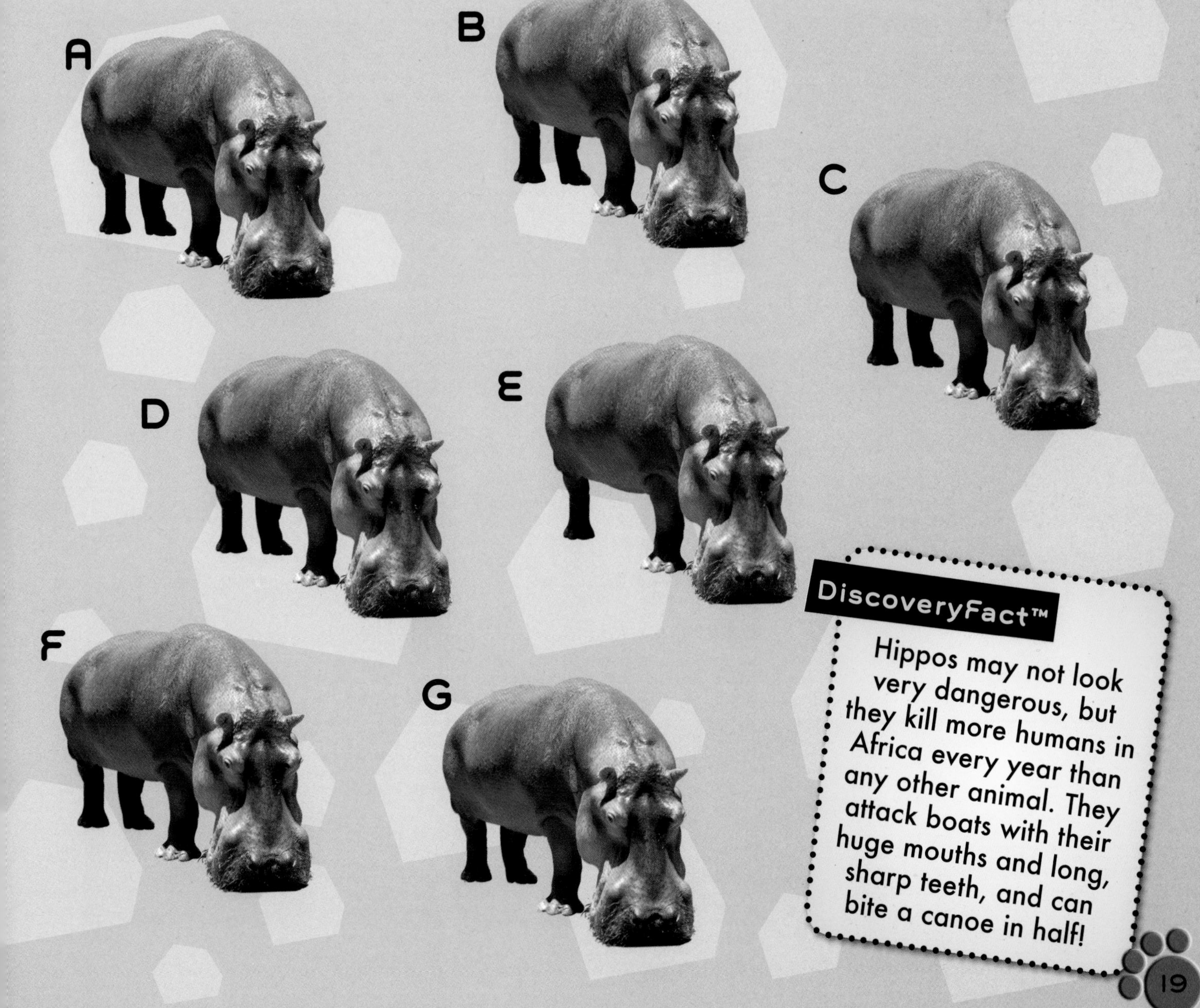

DiscoveryFact™

Hippos may not look very dangerous, but they kill more humans in Africa every year than any other animal. They attack boats with their huge mouths and long, sharp teeth, and can bite a canoe in half!

Big Beast Fact Files

Find the correct stickers to complete these fact files!

Brown Bear

Scientific Name: *Ursus arctos*

Found: Russia, Canada, and North America

Prey: Small mammals and fish

Special Weapons: Huge height and killer paw punch

Polar Bear

Scientific Name: *Ursus maritimus*

Found: Arctic Circle

Prey: Seals and fish

Special Weapon: Biggest land mammal in the world

Hippo

Scientific Name: *Hippopotamus amphibius*

Found: Rivers and lakes in Africa

Prey: Eats plants

Special Weapon: Huge, spearlike teeth

White Rhino

Scientific Name: *Ceratotherium simum*

Found: Southern Africa

Prey: Eats plants and grass

Special Weapon: Charge with lethal horn

Gorilla

Scientific Name: *Gorilla gorilla*

Found: Tropical and subtropical forests

Prey: Eats plants

Special Weapon: Powerful charge

Bull

Scientific Name: *Bos taurus*

Found: Worldwide on farms

Prey: Eats grass

Special Weapon: Fast charge with sharp horns

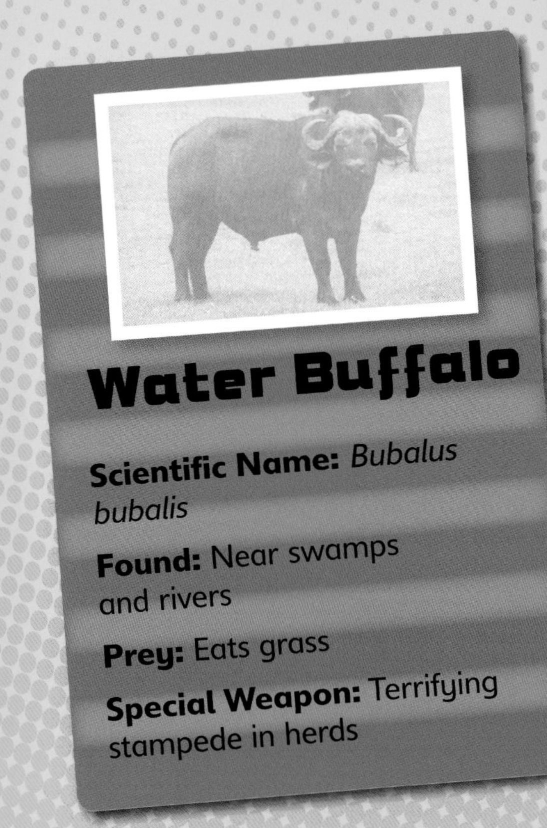

Water Buffalo

Scientific Name: *Bubalus bubalis*

Found: Near swamps and rivers

Prey: Eats grass

Special Weapon: Terrifying stampede in herds

Elk

Scientific Name: *Cervus canadensis*

Found: Forests

Prey: Eats plants

Special Weapon: Big antlers

Shark Complete the Picture

Can you find the correct stickers to complete these pictures of great white sharks?

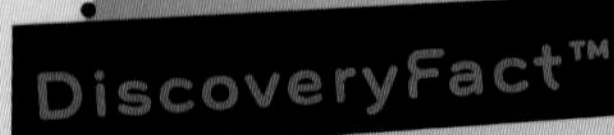

DiscoveryFact™

Great white sharks are the largest predatory fish in the ocean. They have two rows of teeth, and use them like a saw to cut through their prey and kill them.

Barracuda Scramble

Unscramble the letters below to reveal the barracuda's nickname!

r T i e g f o e t h a e s

T _ _ _ _ _ _ t _ _ s _ _

Below are four fish that barracudas like to eat. Find the stickers to complete the page.

DiscoveryFact™

Barracudas are vicious predators, who can attack smaller fish at speeds of up to 25 miles per hour. They have even been known to attack scuba divers with their sharp teeth.

Anchovies

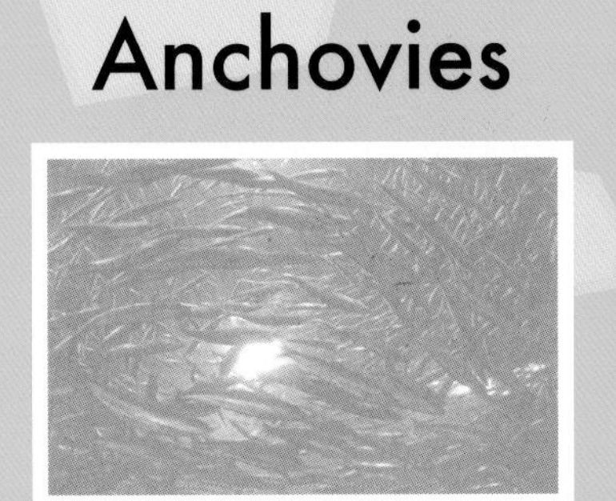

Jack fish

Grouper

Snapper

Giant Cuttlefish Puzzle

Find the correct stickers to complete this giant cuttlefish puzzle. Use the picture clues below to help.

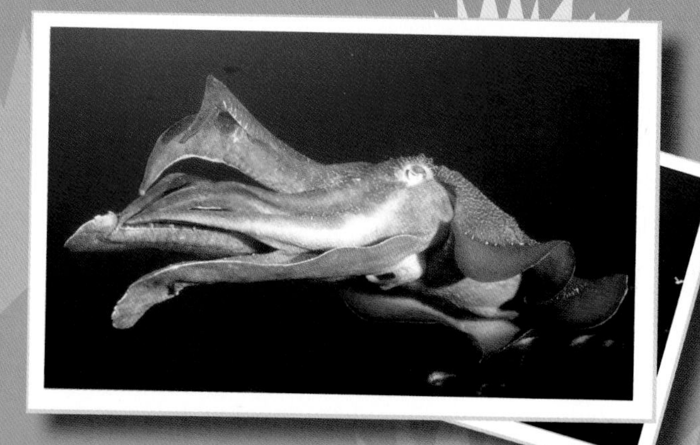

DiscoveryFact™

Giant cuttlefish can change the color of their skin. They do this to communicate with other cuttlefish, to scare off predators, and to camouflage themselves.

Stingray Maze

Can you help this stingray find its way across the seabed to the school of fish? It is hungry and wants to hunt some food!

DiscoveryFact™

Stingrays are very poisonous. The deadly spine on their tail can kill a human—and it remains dangerous even after they have died, it is so toxic.

Start

Finish

Crocodile Code

Use the code breaker to translate the coded message below and discover a cool fact about crocodiles!

A	B	C	D	E	F	G	H	I	J	K	L	M
N	**O**	**P**	**Q**	**R**	**S**	**T**	**U**	**V**	**W**	**X**	**Y**	**Z**

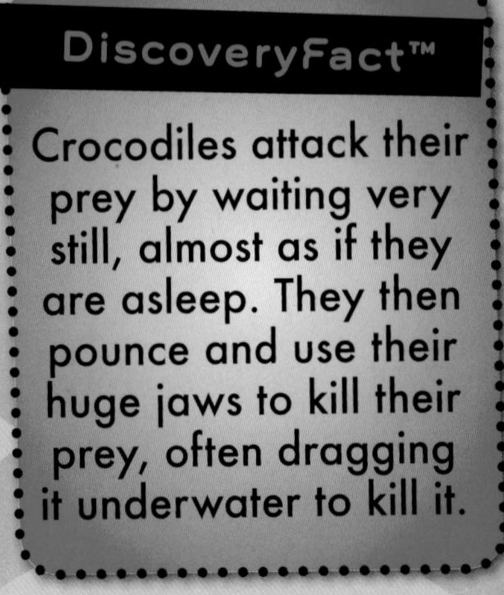

DiscoveryFact™

Crocodiles attack their prey by waiting very still, almost as if they are asleep. They then pounce and use their huge jaws to kill their prey, often dragging it underwater to kill it.

Hammerhead Shark Tangle

This hammerhead shark can smell some prey, but it doesn't know which way to go across the ocean floor. See if you can help it out!

A B C

DiscoveryFact™

Hammerhead sharks have special sensors in their funny-shaped heads that detect the electricity given off by living beings. This makes them very good at detecting possible prey hidden in the sand on the ocean floor.

The correct line is ____.

Killer Whale Odd-One-Out

Each pod of killer whales has an odd one out. Write which one is different in the box at the end of each row.

A B C D

A B C D

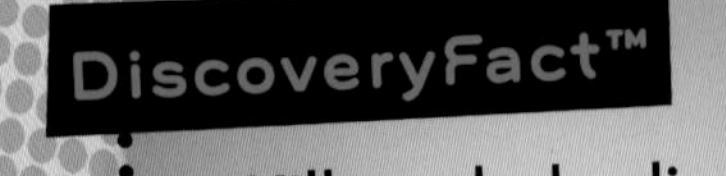

Killer whales live and hunt in groups called "pods." They attack their prey from different angles and use their interlocking teeth to kill and eat it.

Alligator Find-the-Difference

Can you find the four differences between the two alligator images below?

DiscoveryFact™

Alligators have incredibly strong jaws, and bony plates on their skin to protect them from other predators. This makes them super tough.

Water Killer Fact Files

Find the correct stickers to complete these fact files!

Great White Shark

Scientific Name: *Carcharodon carcharias*

Found: All major oceans

Prey: Big fish and smaller sharks

Special Weapon: Hundreds of razor-sharp teeth

Barracuda

Scientific Name: *Sphyraena*

Found: Tropical and subtropical oceans

Prey: Smaller fish

Special Weapon: Extremely powerful killer jaws

Alligator

Scientific Name: *Alligatoridae* family

Found: Rivers, lakes, and tropical swamps

Prey: Fish and small mammals

Special Weapons: Thick scales and viselike jaws

Stingray

Scientific Name: *Dasyatidae* family

Found: Tropical coastal waters

Prey: Small fish and shellfish

Special Weapon: Long, sharp sting and venom

Crocodile

Scientific Name: *Crocodilus* species

Found: Rivers, lakes, and tropical swamps

Prey: Fish, reptiles, and mammals

Special Weapon: Crushing jaws with razor sharp teeth

Killer Whale

Scientific Name: *Orcinus orca*

Found: All oceans

Prey: Sea lions, small whales, seals

Special Weapons: Enormous size and huge mouth

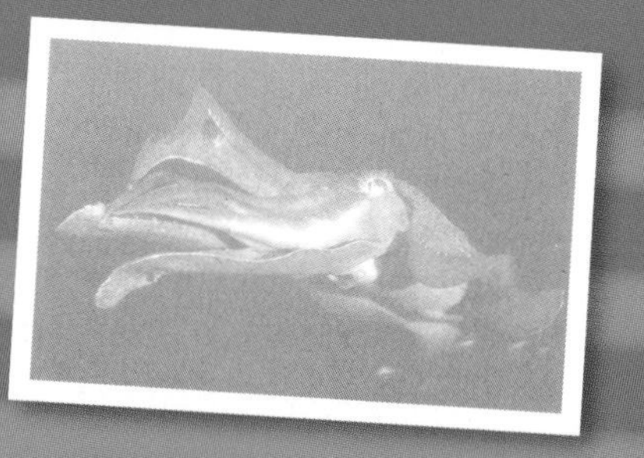

Giant Cuttlefish

Scientific Name: *Sepia apama*

Found: Off the Australian coast

Prey: Small fish and shellfish

Special Weapons: Two suckered tentacles that can be shot out at high speed to grab prey, and a beak to crush prey once caught.

Hammerhead Shark

Scientific Name: *Zygaena malleus*

Found: Warm oceans

Prey: Fish and sea creatures

Special Weapon: Wide head helps track down prey

Scorpion Message

Follow each line to match the letters with the boxes. You will reveal a message about how dangerous a scorpion can be!

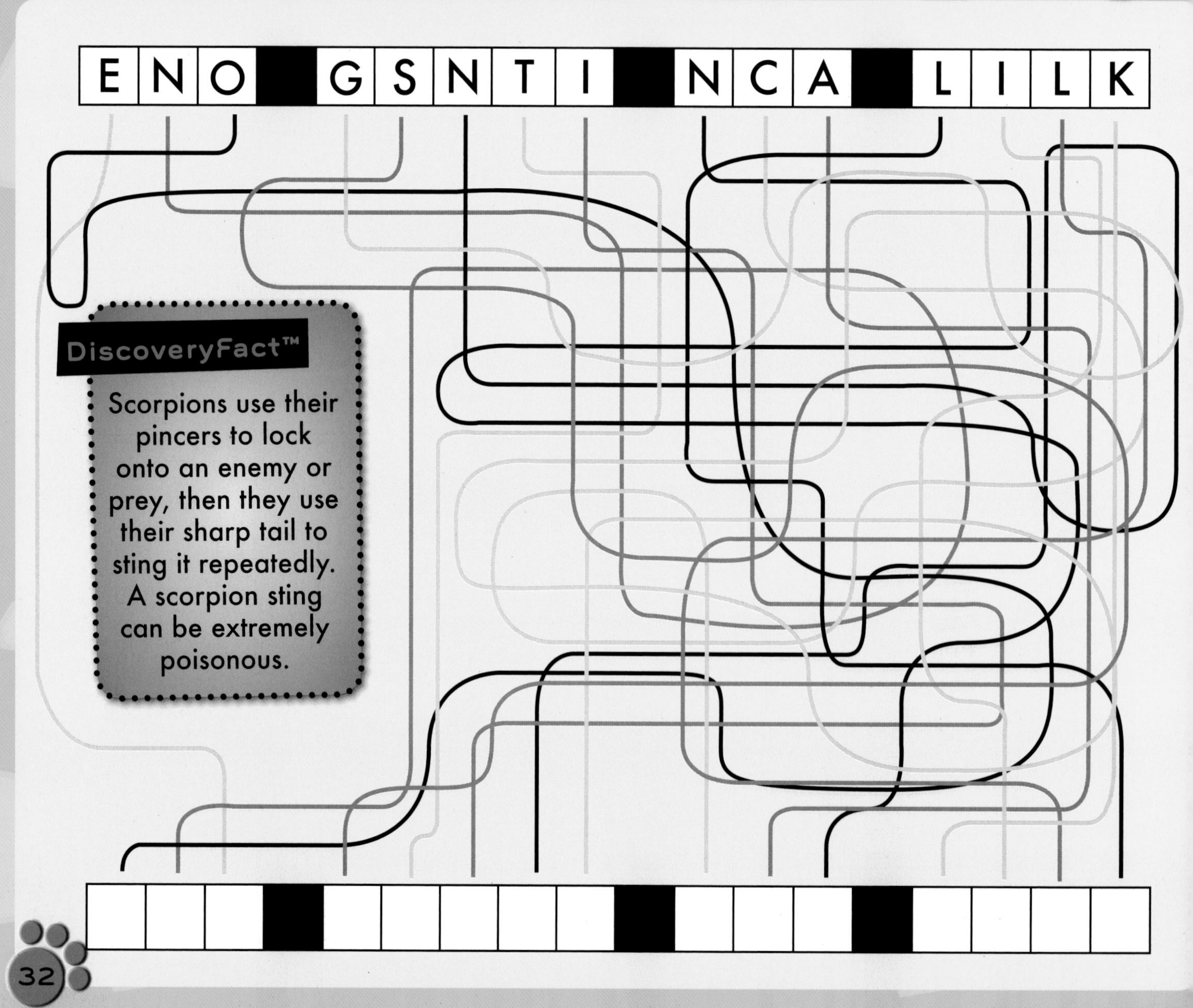

DiscoveryFact™

Scorpions use their pincers to lock onto an enemy or prey, then they use their sharp tail to sting it repeatedly. A scorpion sting can be extremely poisonous.

Stickers For Activities

Stickers For Fun

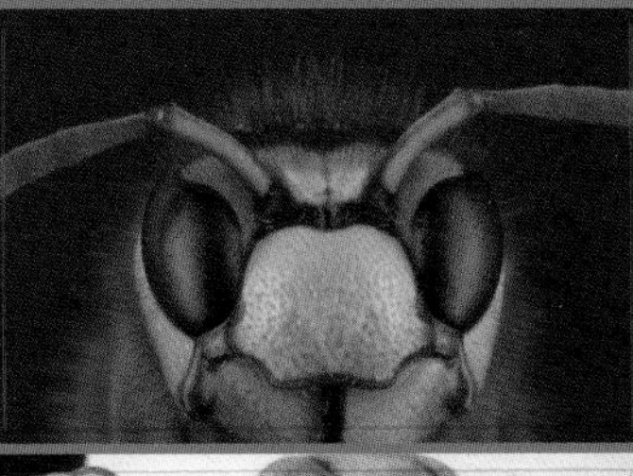

Tarantula Shadows

Can you match each spider to its shadow? Draw lines to match them. There are four pairs in all.

A

1

B

2

C

3

4

D

iscoveryFact™

Tarantulas don't just eat insects. They can kill and eat much bigger animals, such as birds, mice, and rats!

Black Widow Maze

Help this black widow find its way through its web to the fly it is going to eat!

DiscoveryFact™

Black widow spiders are very small, but that doesn't mean that they aren't dangerous. They are extremely poisonous, and a bite from one of these tiny creatures can even kill a human being.

Start

Wolf Spider Scramble

Unscramble the word below to reveal what wolf spiders hunt down and eat.

E I S C T S N

_ _ _ _ _ _ _

Now design a sign warning that there are deadly spiders in the area in this space:

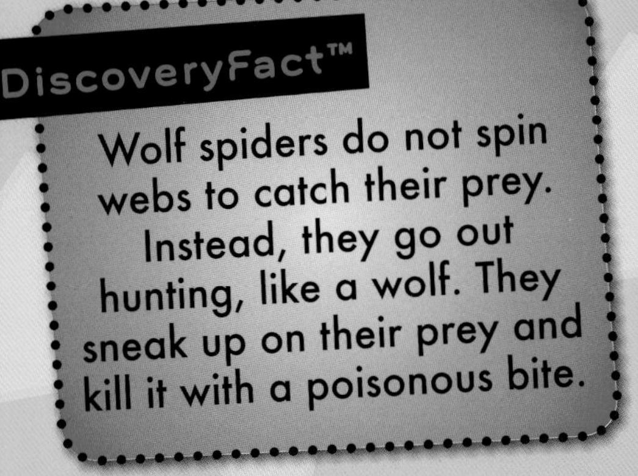

Rattlesnake Word Search

Can you find the ten words below hidden in the grid? They are all things from the rattlesnake's desert home.

SAND
DUNE
CACTUS
OASIS
HEAT
PALM TREE
ROCK
DUST
SNAKES
LIZARDS

Q	E	D	U	N	E	U	I	I	O	P
L	K	H	A	F	J	S	A	N	D	X
H	C	B	K	N	S	M	G	E	S	E
C	O	U	C	A	C	T	U	S	U	G
L	R	K	I	S	L	O	T	V	L	A
B	K	L	E	Y	T	S	C	G	I	R
P	A	L	M	T	R	E	E	L	Z	G
R	D	U	S	T	N	Y	H	S	A	A
K	N	B	C	Z	X	V	E	J	R	D
S	N	A	K	E	S	J	A	T	D	T
Y	O	A	S	I	S	Y	T	S	S	C

DiscoveryFact™

Rattlesnakes make their famous rattling noise by shaking the tip of their tail, which has a chain of hollow 'beads' made from special scales. The rattle warns any enemies that the snake is ready to bite!

Boa Constrictor Blurs

This boa constrictor has been in a feeding frenzy! Look at the blurred pictures below and write the name of each animal it has had for dinner under the picture.

Toucan   Spider monkey   Tapir   Rat

1

2

3
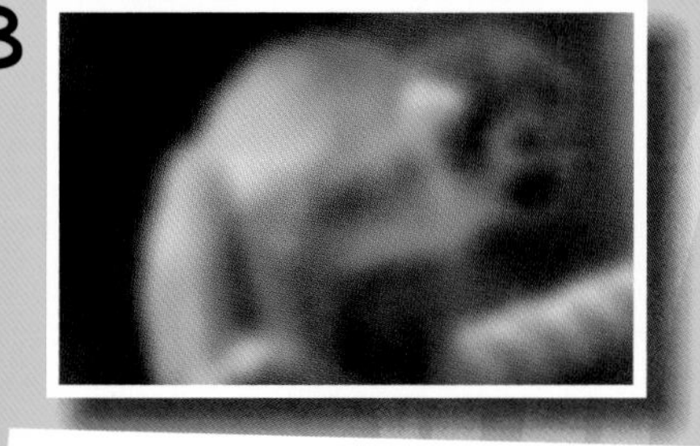

4
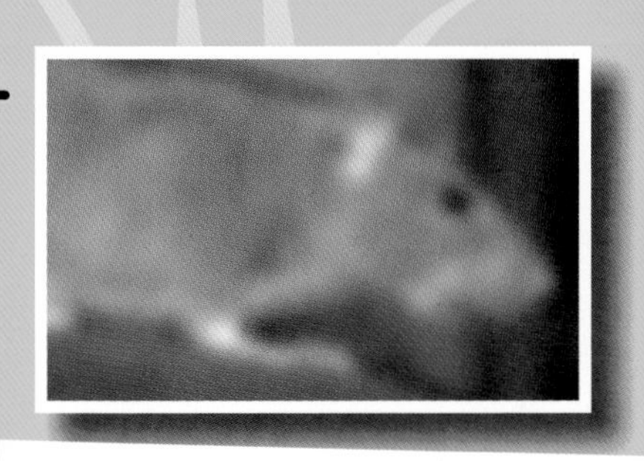

Now find an in-focus picture of each animal on the sticker sheets and put them in this space:

DiscoveryFact™

Boa constrictors don't bite their prey. They crush it to death by wrapping themselves around it and suffocating it.

Python Number Puzzle

Crack these number puzzles to find out some cool facts about pythons. Do the math to reveal the answer to the questions below!

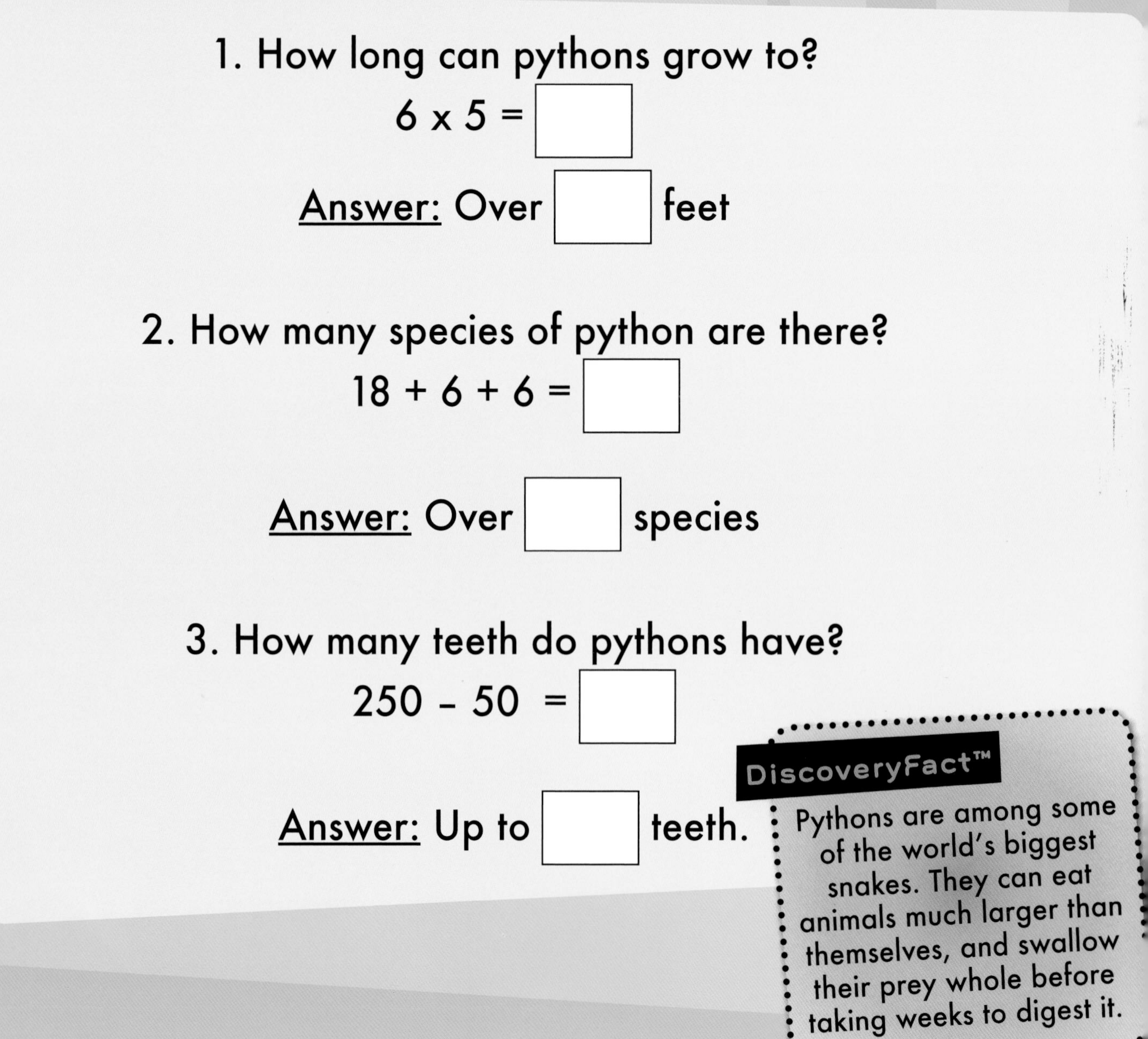

1. How long can pythons grow to?

6 x 5 = ☐

<u>Answer:</u> Over ☐ feet

2. How many species of python are there?

18 + 6 + 6 = ☐

<u>Answer:</u> Over ☐ species

3. How many teeth do pythons have?

250 - 50 = ☐

<u>Answer:</u> Up to ☐ teeth.

DiscoveryFact™

Pythons are among some of the world's biggest snakes. They can eat animals much larger than themselves, and swallow their prey whole before taking weeks to digest it.

Cobra Puzzle

Find the correct stickers to complete this cobra puzzle! Use the picture clues below to help.

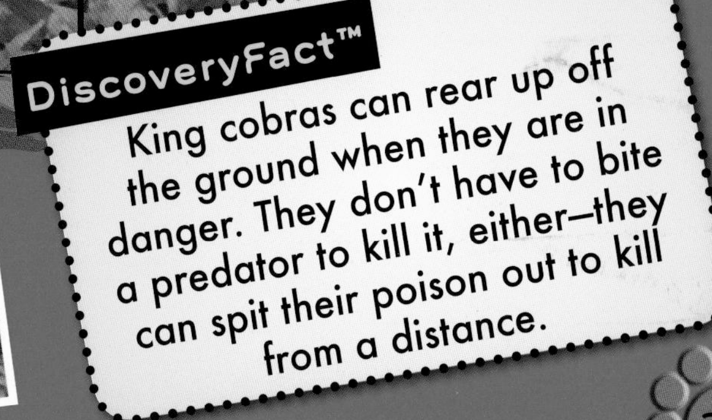

DiscoveryFact™

King cobras can rear up off the ground when they are in danger. They don't have to bite a predator to kill it, either—they can spit their poison out to kill from a distance.

Crawler and Slitherer Fact Files

Find the correct stickers to complete these fact files!

Scorpion

Scientific Name: *Scorpiones*

Found: Worldwide

Prey: Insects

Special Weapons: Powerful pincers and venomous sting

Wolf Spider

Scientific Name: *Lycosidae* family

Found: Worldwide

Prey: Smaller insects

Special Weapon: Venomous sting

Black Widow

Scientific Name: *Latrodectus*

Found: North America

Prey: Insects and other spiders

Special Weapon: Deadly poison

Tarantula

Scientific Name: *Theraphosidae*

Found: Warm regions worldwide

Prey: Can eat birds and small mammals

Special Weapon: Strong silk web to catch prey

Boa Constrictor

Scientific Name: *Boa constrictor*

Found: Central and South America

Prey: Large lizards and mammals

Special Weapon: Crushes victims to death with vise-like grip

Python

Scientific Name: *Pythonidae*

Found: African and Asian tropics

Prey: Animals as big as goats and gazelles

Special Weapon: Body can stretch to eat prey whole

Rattlesnake

Scientific Name: *Crotalus and Sistrurus* species

Found: Deserts

Prey: Birds and small animals

Special Weapon: Rattle on end of tail to scare off predators

King Cobra

Scientific Name: *Naja naja*

Found: Asian tropical regions

Prey: Other snakes and small mammals

Special Weapon: Can spit venom to kill prey from a distance

Hyena Hidden Message

Cross out the numbers and the capital letters below. Write all the small letters that are left out in the spaces underneath to reveal where hyenas come from.

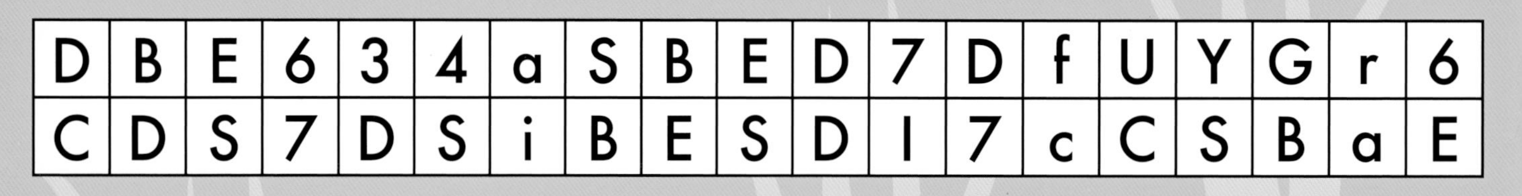

D	B	E	6	3	4	a	S	B	E	D	7	D	f	U	Y	G	r	6
C	D	S	7	D	S	i	B	E	S	D	I	7	c	C	S	B	a	E

Below are two animals that hyenas like to eat. Find the stickers to complete the page.

DiscoveryFact™

Hyenas are so tough, they even eat the bones of their prey. The strong teeth of these fierce animals crush them up so they can be digested.

Zebra

Wildebeest

Wild Dog Maze

This wild dog has been separated from his pack while hunting. Help him find his way back by completing this tricky maze!

Start

Finish

DiscoveryFact™

Wild dogs hunt in packs of up to 20 dogs. They attack together to overcome much bigger animals, before feasting on them together. They can kill animals as big as zebras.

Jackal Find-the-Difference

Can you find the four differences between the two jackal pictures below?

DiscoveryFact™

Jackals often live in holes in the ground, or dens, made by other animals. They come out to hunt their prey, or to steal food from kills made by other animals, such as lions or tigers.

Coyote Shadows

Find a sticker to match the picture below and put it on the page. Then circle the shadow that matches the sticker exactly.

DiscoveryFact™

Coyotes howl loudly to talk to each other. They can run for miles at high speeds, and can tire out their prey with a long chase before killing and eating it.

Arctic Fox Code

Arctic foxes are fierce, but they aren't the scariest animals in the Arctic. Use the code breaker to translate the coded message below and discover the Arctic fox's biggest threat!

DiscoveryFact™

Arctic foxes' fur changes to a darker gray in the summer so that they stay camouflaged, even without the snow.

Wolf Odd-One-Out

Take a close look at the group of wolves below. One of them isn't the same as the others. Can you circle the odd one out?

A

B

C

D

E

F

G

DiscoveryFact™

Wolves howl to talk to each other and to mark out their territory. They hunt and kill deer and other animals, using their sharp teeth to bite their prey until it becomes weak and collapses.

Pit Bull Puzzle

Find the correct stickers to complete this pit bull puzzle! Use the picture clues below to help.

DiscoveryFact™

These fierce dogs were bred for fighting hundreds of years ago. They have incredibly strong jaws and can kill large animals or people with their bite.

Which Fox Comes Next?

Take a look at the rows of foxes below. Figure out which color should come next in each series, and use your stickers to fill it in!

DiscoveryFact™

Many foxes have adapted to living in cities, and feed on rats, mice, and garbage left by human beings.

Four-Legged Hunter Fact Files

Find the correct stickers to complete these fact files!

Hyena

Scientific Name: *Hyaena* and *Crocuta* species

Found: African savannas

Prey: Mammals as big as zebras

Special Weapon: Strong teeth to crack through victims' bones

Wild Dog

Scientific Name: *Lycaon pictus*

Found: African savannas

Prey: Deer and other mammals

Special Weapon: Hunting in packs to bring down large prey

Jackal

Scientific Name: *Canis aureus*

Found: Africa and Asia

Prey: Birds, reptiles, and small mammals

Special Weapon: Can run for miles without getting tired

Coyote

Scientific Name: *Canis latrans*

Found: North America

Prey: Squirrels, mice, and small animals

Special Weapon: Can hunt for up to 21 hours at a time

Arctic Fox

Scientific Name: *Vulpes lagopus*

Found: Arctic circle

Prey: Any animals it can find in the snow

Special Weapon: Fur changes color according to season

Wolf

Scientific Name: *Canis lupus*

Found: Worldwide

Prey: Sheep, goats, pigs, and deer

Special Weapon: Very tough—can live for 17 days without food

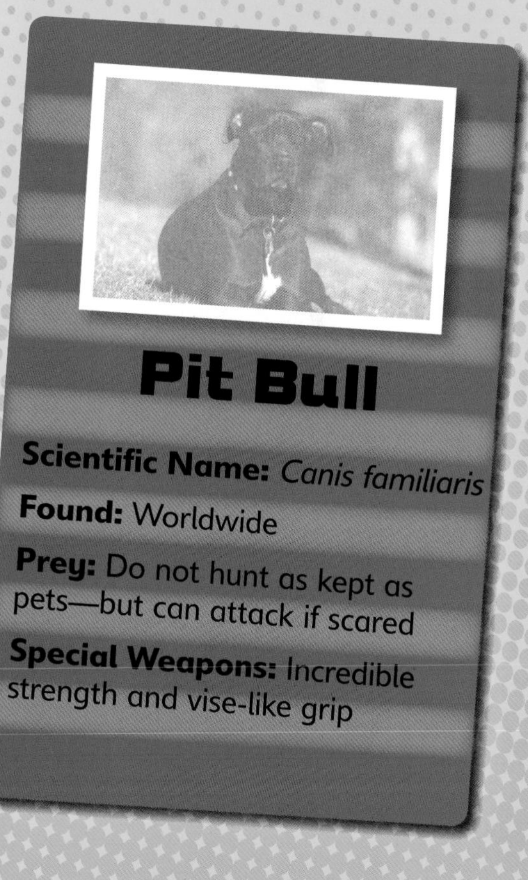

Pit Bull

Scientific Name: *Canis familiaris*

Found: Worldwide

Prey: Do not hunt as kept as pets—but can attack if scared

Special Weapons: Incredible strength and vise-like grip

Fox

Scientific Name: *Vulpes vulpes*

Found: Worldwide

Prey: Rabbits and small mammals

Special Weapon: Special pounce to attack prey

Golden Eagle Wordsearch

See if you can find these ten things golden eagles eat hidden in the squares below.

HARE
RABBIT
MOUSE
VOLE
MOLE
DEER
MARMOT
FOX
BIRD
GOAT

Q	M	T	G	M	A	R	M	O	T	P
L	O	H	A	R	E	S	A	O	Z	X
I	L	B	A	N	L	M	G	R	S	E
L	E	U	K	O	H	K	O	A	U	G
E	B	I	R	D	I	V	W	B	D	O
Y	K	L	U	Y	T	O	C	B	Q	A
E	E	T	M	U	I	L	P	I	J	T
R	D	L	E	I	L	E	E	T	R	I
F	D	E	E	R	X	V	N	J	G	D
S	A	E	T	M	A	H	F	O	X	T
M	O	U	S	E	N	Y	F	S	D	C

DiscoveryFact™

Golden eagles are hunting birds, and can kill and eat animals as large as young deer and foxes. They kill their prey using their sharp talons, then rip it apart with their strong beaks.

Buzzard Mix-Up

Can you see which way will lead this buzzard to its nest? It has been out tracking down its prey and can't find its way back!

A B C

DiscoveryFact™

Buzzards are very protective about their hunting territory, and will fight other buzzards if they fly into their patch. They need a wide area to hunt in to keep them supplied with the mammals and other animals they eat.

The correct line is ___ .

Peregrine Falcon Puzzle

Find the correct stickers to complete this peregrine falcon puzzle! Use the picture clues below to help.

DiscoveryFact™

Peregrine falcons can hit over 200 miles per hour when diving out of the sky to catch and kill other birds, before eating them with their strong beaks.

Vulture Message

Can you unscramble the words below to reveal a cool fact about vultures? Follow the lines from the letters to put them in the right order!

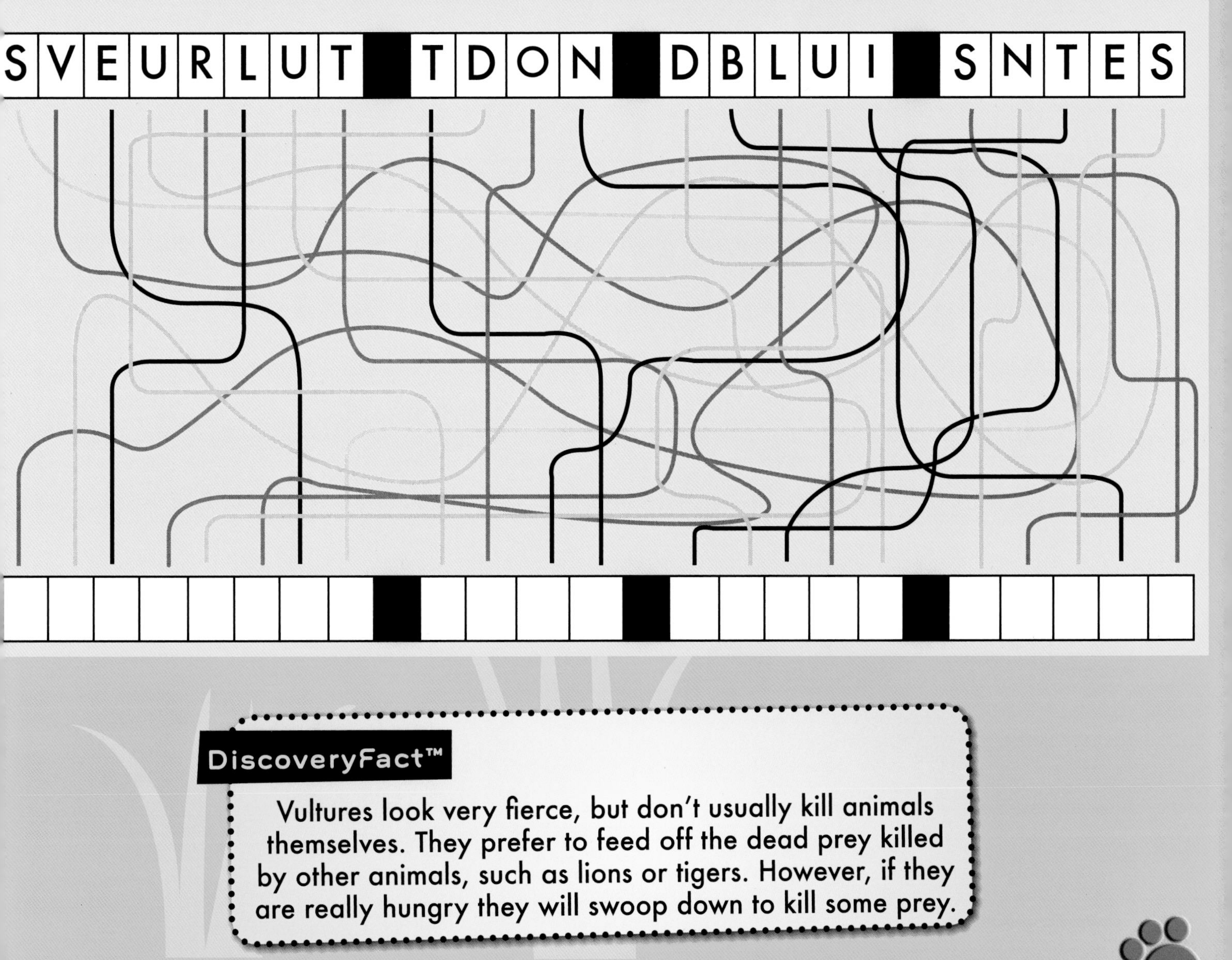

DiscoveryFact™

Vultures look very fierce, but don't usually kill animals themselves. They prefer to feed off the dead prey killed by other animals, such as lions or tigers. However, if they are really hungry they will swoop down to kill some prey.

Vampire Bat Odd-One-Out

Each row of bats below has an odd one out. Circle the bat that is different in each row!

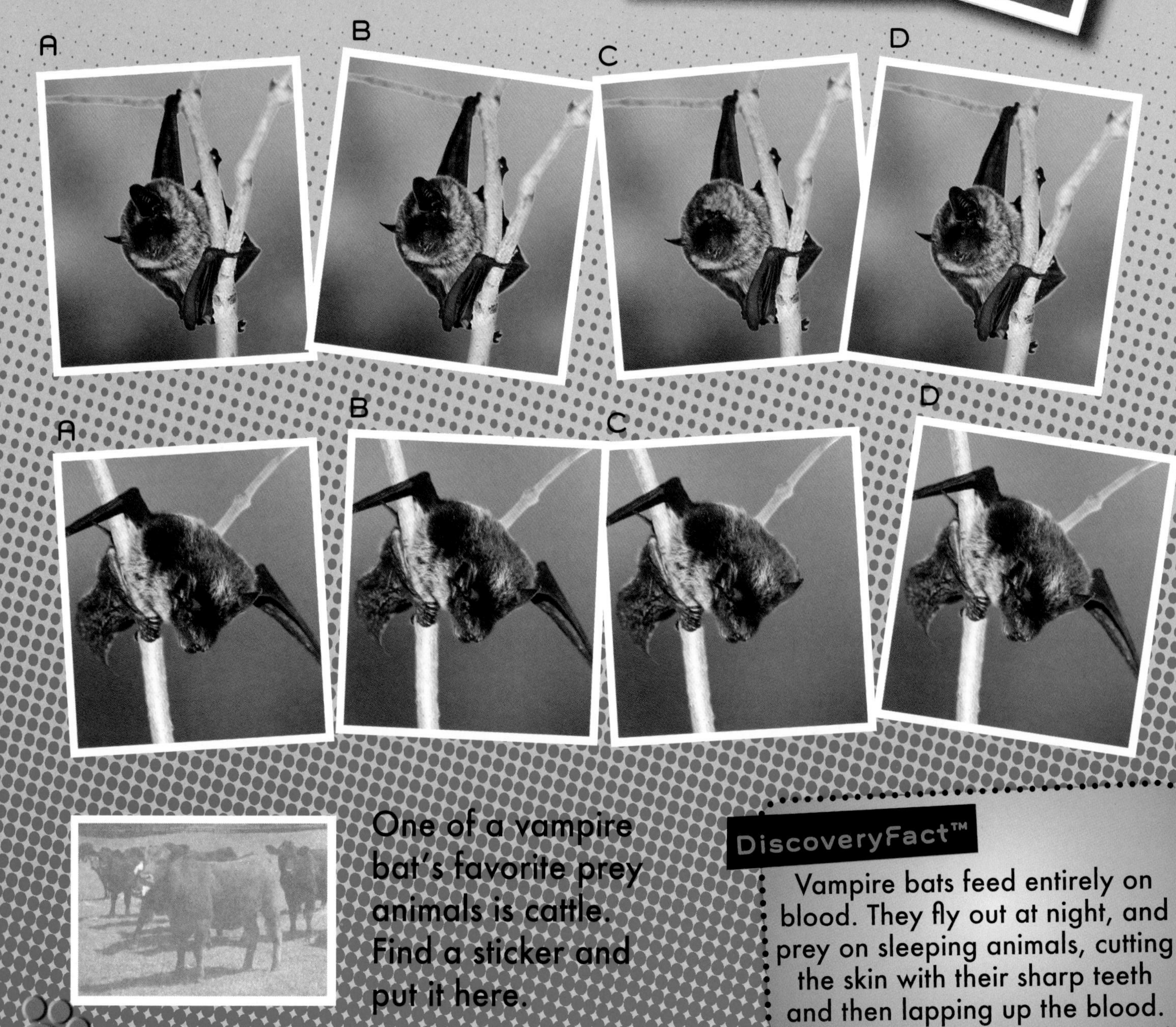

One of a vampire bat's favorite prey animals is cattle. Find a sticker and put it here.

DiscoveryFact™

Vampire bats feed entirely on blood. They fly out at night, and prey on sleeping animals, cutting the skin with their sharp teeth and then lapping up the blood.

Bee Honeycomb

Find your way across the honeycomb maze below by coloring in the boxes to spell out the words "SWARMING BEES."

B	A	K	T	J	I	M	F	S
B	U	H	J	Y	D	H	L	Y
N	X	G	R	L	E	Y	U	O
S	W	A	M	S	O	L	E	R
M	O	G	G	I	N	S	Y	L
W	E	N	H	U	G	G	H	E
P	J	R	Y	R	J	B	L	Y
Y	Y	F	G	S	Y	E	E	S

Start: S (left side)

Finish: S (right side)

DiscoveryFact™

A swarm of giant bees can sting a person to death if they attack. They spring into action if they believe their hive is threatened by a predator!

Some bees make honeycomb to feed their young with. Find a sticker and put it here.

Giant Hornet Puzzle

Find the correct stickers to complete this giant hornet puzzle. Use the picture clues below to help.

DiscoveryFact™

These flying beasts can grow to be 2 inches long, which is huge for an insect. They have a poisonous sting, and they can sting their prey over and over again unlike bees!

Cassowary Maze

Help this big bird find its way back to its eggs. It can't fly, so it needs to get through the maze on foot!

Start

Finish

DiscoveryFact™

These huge birds can't fly—they live on land. They are very strong, and have three long, sharp toes on each foot which they can use to injure and even kill animals or humans that threaten their nests.

Now find the correct sticker to complete the page.

Flying Beasts Fact Files

Find the correct stickers to complete these fact files!

Golden Eagle

Scientific Name: *Aquila chrysaetos*

Found: Northern hemisphere

Prey: Hares, mice, young deer

Special Weapon: Incredible eyesight

Buzzard

Scientific Name: *Buteo buteo*

Found: Europe and Asia

Prey: Small animals, snakes, and lizards

Special Weapon: Sharp claws

Peregrine Falcon

Scientific Name: *Falco peregrinus*

Found: Worldwide

Prey: Other birds

Special Weapon: 200 miles per hour dive-bomb to attack prey

Vulture

Scientific Name: *Accipitridae/ Cathartidae*

Found: Worldwide

Prey: Feeds on dead animals

Special Weapon: Strong talons

Vampire Bat

Scientific Name: *Desmodus rotundus*

Found: In dark caves worldwide

Prey: Large mammals, such as horses or people

Special Weapon: Sucks blood while prey sleeps

Giant Hornet

Scientific Name: *Vespa mandarinia*

Found: Southeast Asia

Prey: Eats plants

Special Weapon: Large, poisonous stinger can be used again and again

Bee

Scientific Name: *Apoidea* family

Found: Worldwide

Prey: Eats honey and plant matter

Special Weapon: Painful sting

Cassowary

Scientific Name: *Casuarius* species

Found: Australia

Prey: Small animals

Special Weapon: Sharp, spiky feet kick predators

Answers

PAGE 2

D	E	E	R	D	T	R	Y	I	O	P
A	D	G	J	K	A	L	Z	X	E	C
N	M	Q	E	T	P	U	I	E	P	F
T	A	P	I	R	S	Q	H	S	F	O
H	K	M	L	Z	C	S	B	O	M	X
C	R	O	C	O	D	I	L	E	S	E
A	P	N	I	Y	R	E	J	L	R	S
T	A	K	F	L	Q	J	Z	Q	E	R
T	C	E	I	T	U	R	T	L	E	S
L	C	Y	S	A	L	E	L	S	P	R
E	G	S	H	B	I	R	D	S	A	Q

PAGE 3

PAGE 4
Cheetahs are the fastest land mammals.

PAGE 5
The correct line is A.

PAGE 6
The odd one out is C.

PAGE 7
Leopards hide their prey in trees.

PAGE 9
The following pairs match: A and 3, B and 1, C and 2

PAGE 12
A brown bear's most deadly weapon is its <u>claws</u>.
Brown bears are <u>nocturnal</u>.
95 percent of the U.S. brown bear population lives in <u>Alaska</u>.

PAGE 13

Q	A	T	G	Y	F	U	I	I	O	P
L	R	H	L	F	I	S	A	C	Z	X
I	C	B	A	N	S	M	G	E	S	E
C	T	U	C	O	H	K	O	U	U	G
E	I	K	I	S	N	O	W	V	D	A
B	C	L	E	Y	T	S	C	A	V	E
E	F	T	R	U	I	O	P	L	J	G
R	O	R	E	I	N	D	E	E	R	A
G	X	B	C	Z	X	V	N	J	G	D
S	A	E	T	G	S	E	A	L	U	T
Y	E	S	E	A	N	Y	F	S	D	C

PAGE 14

A running herd of buffalo is called a <u>stampede</u>.

PAGE 16
The correct line is A.

PAGE 17
Silverback

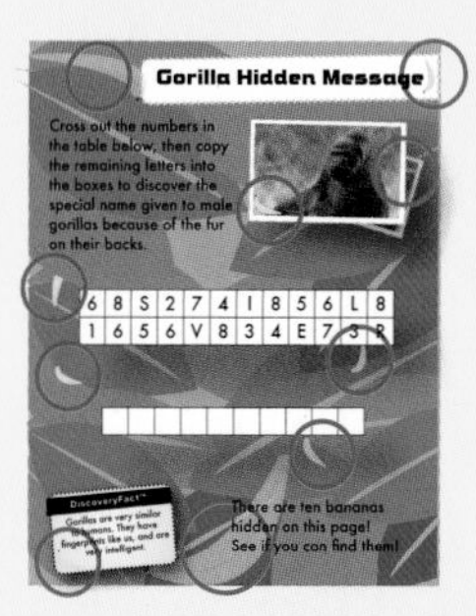

PAGE 18
The following pairs match: A and F, E and B, C and G.

PAGE 19
E is the odd one out.

PAGE 23
Tiger of the sea

PAGE 25

PAGE 26
Crocodiles have up to seventy teeth.

PAGE 27
The correct line is A.

PAGE 28
Row 1: C is the odd one out
Row 2: D is the odd one out

PAGE 29

PAGE 32
One sting can kill.

PAGE 33
The following pairs match: A and 3, B and 4, C and 2, D and 1.

PAGE 34

PAGE 35

Insects

PAGE 36

Q	E	D	U	N	E	U	I	I	O	P
L	K	H	A	F	J	S	A	N	D	X
H	C	B	K	N	S	M	G	E	S	E
C	O	U	C	A	C	T	U	S	U	G
L	R	K	I	S	L	O	T	V	L	A
B	K	L	E	Y	T	S	C	G	I	R
P	A	L	M	T	R	E	E	L	Z	G
R	D	U	S	T	N	Y	H	S	A	A
K	N	B	C	Z	X	V	E	J	R	D
S	N	A	K	E	S	J	A	T	D	T
Y	O	A	S	I	S	Y	T	S	S	C

PAGE 37

1. Tapir
2. Toucan
3. Spider monkey
4. Rat

PAGE 38

1. Over 30 feet
2. Over 30 species
3. Up to 200 teeth

PAGE 42

Africa

PAGE 43

PAGE 44

PAGE 45

B matches the picture exactly.

PAGE 46

Polar bear

PAGE 47

C is the odd one out

PAGE 49

First row: Blue
Second row: Yellow
Third row: Red

PAGE 52

Q	M	T	G	M	A	R	M	O	T	P
L	O	H	A	R	E	S	A	O	Z	X
I	L	B	A	N	L	M	G	R	S	E
L	E	U	K	O	H	K	O	A	U	G
E	B	I	R	D	I	V	W	B	D	O
Y	K	L	U	Y	T	O	C	B	Q	A
E	E	T	M	U	I	L	P	I	J	T
R	D	L	E	I	L	E	E	T	R	I
F	D	E	E	R	X	V	N	J	G	D
S	A	E	T	M	A	H	F	O	X	T
M	O	U	S	E	N	Y	F	S	D	C

PAGE 53

The correct line is A.

PAGE 55

Vultures don't build nests.

PAGE 56

Row 1: C is the odd one out
Row 2: C is the odd one out

PAGE 57

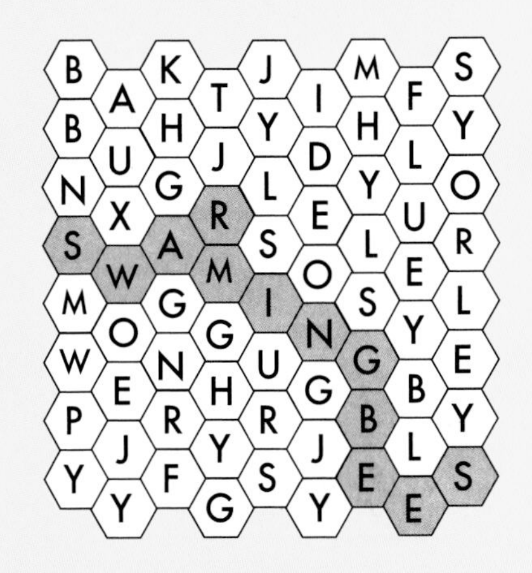

PAGE 59

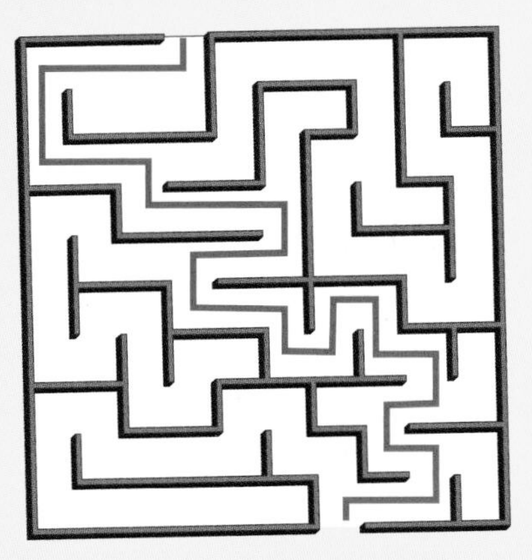

Acknowledgments

Cover: clockwise from top left: Dreamstime, Dreamtime/Larry Powell, Dreamstime, Dreamstime/Raycart, Dreamstime/Bizarzoo, Dreamstime/Carolyne Pehora, Corbis/DLILLC, Dreamstime/Stephenmeese, Corbis/Tom Brakefield, Dreamstime/Kaikai, Dreamstime/Kwerry, Dreamstime/Martina Berg, Corbis/DLILLC

1 left Corbis/DLILLC, 1 middle Dreamstime/Raycart, 1 right Dreamstime/Kwerry, 2 Dreamstime/Ferenc Cegledi, 3 top Dreamstime, 3 bottom Giorgio Perbellini, 4 Corbis, 5 Dreamstime/Stephenmeese, 7 top istockphoto/Alexander Hafemann, 7 bottom Dreamstime/Jayarman, 8 istockphoto/rphotos, 9 top istockphoto/Anna Yu, 9 middle left istockphoto/Eric Isselée, 9 middle centre istockphoto/Eric Isselée, 9 middle right istockphoto/Eric Isselée, 12 istockphoto/BostjanT, 13 Dreamstime/Carolyn Pehora, 14 top istockphoto/Jonathan Weiner, 14 middle istockphoto/Steve Lovegrove, 15 istockphoto/Robert Rushton, 16 top istockphoto/Justin Horrocks, 16 bottom istockphoto/Pamela Moore, 17 Dreamstime/Martina Berg, 18 istockphoto/Paul Tessier, 19 top istockphoto/Dan Rowley, 19 middle istockphoto/Karim Hesham, 22 top istockphoto/Keith Flood, 22 middle left istockphoto/Chris Dascher, 22 middle right istockphoto/Keith Flood, 22 bottom left istockphoto/Chuck Babbitt, 22 bottom right istockphoto/Keith Flood, 23 top istockphoto/Richard Brooks, 23 middle left istockphoto/Nikontiger, 23 middle right istockphoto/breckeni, 23 bottom left istockphoto/Klaas Lingbeek, 23 bottom right istockphoto/David Safanda, 24 Corbis/Gary Bell/zefa, 25 top istockphoto/Mark Kostich, 26 istockphoto/kevdog818, 27 istockphoto/Ian Scott, 28 istockphoto/Evgeniya Lazareva, 29 istockphoto/Nancy Nehring, 30 Dreamstime, 31 istockphoto/John Bell, 34 Dreamstime/Dawn Allyn, 35 Dreamstime/Michael Pettigrew, 36 Dreamtime/Stephen McSweeny, 37 top Dreamstime, 37 middle left istockphoto/Holger Ehler, 37 middle istockphoto/Michael Peck, 37 right istockphoto/Ivan Cholakov, 37 bottom istockphoto/kevdog818, 38 istockphoto/poco_bw, 39 istockphoto/Chromix, 42 Dreamstime, 43 istockphoto/Lee Pettet, 44 istockphoto/Bruce Block, 45 top istockphoto/Denis Pepin, 45 middle istockphoto/Montreal_photos, 46 istockphoto/Jeffrey Hochstrasser, 47 istockphoto/Andy Gehrig, 48 istockphoto/Linda Charlton, 49 istockphoto/Dmitry Deshevykh, 52 istockphoto/Missing35mm, 53 istockphoto/Pawel Spychala, 54 istockphoto/Missing35mm, 55 istockphoto/Guenter Guni, 56 top Dreamstime/Adam Booth, 56 middle istockphoto/Alexei Zaycev, 57 istockphoto/Nathan McClunie, 58 Dreamstime/Vladvitek, 59 istockphoto/Ian Scott

Written by Matt Crossick

First published by Parragon in 2009

Parragon
Queen Street House
4 Queen Street
Bath BA1 1HE, UK

ISBN 978-1-4075-7442-4

Printed in China